THIS BOOK BELONGS TO:

CONTACT INFORMATION

NAME: Jessica Lewis

ADDRESS: 5712 Wilder Ridge
Austin, TX 78759

PHONE: 512·963·1013

START / END DATES

2 / 17 / 2021 TO   /   /

DEDICATION

This Dog Training Log Journal Log book is dedicated to all the dog owners out there who love their pets, want to train them, and document their findings in the process.

You are my inspiration for producing books and I'm honored to be a part of keeping all of your Dog Training notes and records organized.

This journal notebook will help you record your details about training your dog.

Thoughtfully put together with these sections to record: Contact Info Page, Pet Information, Pet Sitter Notes, Vaccinations Record, Vet Visits, Feeding Schedule, Daily Responsibility Chart, and Training Log.

HOW TO USE THIS BOOK

The purpose of this book is to keep all of your Dog Training notes all in one place. It will help keep you organized.

This Dog Training Log Journal will allow you to accurately document every detail about training your dog or puppy. It's a great way to chart your course through training your dog, puppy or service dog.

Here are examples of the prompts for you to fill in and write about your experience in this book:

1. **Contact Info Page** – For writing the owner's contact information and the veterinary info.

2. **Pet Information** – All your dog's info including Name, Date of Birth, Age, Weight, Sex, Breed, Color, Markings, Food Brand, Treat Brand, Breeder/ Shelter, Notes.

3. **Pet Sitter Notes** – Write Where You'll Be, Phone, Address, Notes, Emergency Contact, Special Instructions.

4. **Vaccinations Record** – Log the Date, Vaccination, and Vet.

5. **Vet Visits** – Record Date, Reason for Visit, and Vet.

6. **Feeding Schedule** – Write Morning Time, Evening Time, and Amount for each day of the week.

7. **Daily Responsibility Chart** – For writing your own chore list for each day of the week with checkboxes.

8. **Training Log** – Note the Date, Time, Handler, Location, Type of Training, Weather, Temperature, Task Type, Duration, Treat or Rewards Used, Competency/ Obedience Level, Success, Needs Improvement, and Notes.

PET INFO

PET NAME: | DATE OF BIRTH:

AGE: | WEIGHT: | SEX: ☐ MALE ☐ FEMALE

BREED:

COLOR:

MARKINGS:

FOOD BRAND: | SERVING:

TREAT BRAND | SERVING:

BREEDER/SHELTER

PHONE #:

ADOPTION DATE:

NOTES:

PET SITTER NOTES

WHERE WE'LL BE

PHONE#:
_____

ADDRESS:
_____

NOTES:
_____
_____
_____
_____

EMERGENCY CONTACT

NAME:
_____

PHONE#:
_____

WORK#:
_____

ADDRESS:
_____

NOTES
_____
_____
_____
_____

SPECIAL INSTRUCTIONS:
_____
_____
_____
_____
_____
_____

VACCINATIONS

DATE:	VACCINATION:	VET

VET VISITS

DATE:	REASON FOR VISIT	VET

FEEDING SCHEDULE

							MORNING TIME	EVENING TIME	AMOUNT
S	M	T	W	T	F	S			
☐	☐	☐	☐	☐	☐	☐			
S	M	T	W	T	F	S			
☐	☐	☐	☐	☐	☐	☐			
S	M	T	W	T	F	S			
☐	☐	☐	☐	☐	☐	☐			
S	M	T	W	T	F	S			
☐	☐	☐	☐	☐	☐	☐			
S	M	T	W	T	F	S			
☐	☐	☐	☐	☐	☐	☐			
S	M	T	W	T	F	S			
☐	☐	☐	☐	☐	☐	☐			
S	M	T	W	T	F	S			
☐	☐	☐	☐	☐	☐	☐			
S	M	T	W	T	F	S			
☐	☐	☐	☐	☐	☐	☐			
S	M	T	W	T	F	S			
☐	☐	☐	☐	☐	☐	☐			
S	M	T	W	T	F	S			
☐	☐	☐	☐	☐	☐	☐			
S	M	T	W	T	F	S			
☐	☐	☐	☐	☐	☐	☐			
S	M	T	W	T	F	S			
☐	☐	☐	☐	☐	☐	☐			
S	M	T	W	T	F	S			
☐	☐	☐	☐	☐	☐	☐			
S	M	T	W	T	F	S			
☐	☐	☐	☐	☐	☐	☐			
S	M	T	W	T	F	S			
☐	☐	☐	☐	☐	☐	☐			
S	M	T	W	T	F	S			
☐	☐	☐	☐	☐	☐	☐			
S	M	T	W	T	F	S			
☐	☐	☐	☐	☐	☐	☐			
S	M	T	W	T	F	S			
☐	☐	☐	☐	☐	☐	☐			
S	M	T	W	T	F	S			
☐	☐	☐	☐	☐	☐	☐			

RESPONSIBILITY CHART

HORE

	S	M	T	W	T	F	S
	☐	☐	☐	☐	☐	☐	☐
	S	M	T	W	T	F	S
	☐	☐	☐	☐	☐	☐	☐
	S	M	T	W	T	F	S
	☐	☐	☐	☐	☐	☐	☐
	S	M	T	W	T	F	S
	☐	☐	☐	☐	☐	☐	☐
	S	M	T	W	T	F	S
	☐	☐	☐	☐	☐	☐	☐
	S	M	T	W	T	F	S
	☐	☐	☐	☐	☐	☐	☐
	S	M	T	W	T	F	S
	☐	☐	☐	☐	☐	☐	☐
	S	M	T	W	T	F	S
	☐	☐	☐	☐	☐	☐	☐
	S	M	T	W	T	F	S
	☐	☐	☐	☐	☐	☐	☐
	S	M	T	W	T	F	S
	☐	☐	☐	☐	☐	☐	☐
	S	M	T	W	T	F	S
	☐	☐	☐	☐	☐	☐	☐
	S	M	T	W	T	F	S
	☐	☐	☐	☐	☐	☐	☐
	S	M	T	W	T	F	S
	☐	☐	☐	☐	☐	☐	☐
	S	M	T	W	T	F	S
	☐	☐	☐	☐	☐	☐	☐
	S	M	T	C W	T	F	S
	☐	☐	☐	☐	☐	☐	☐
	S	M	T	W	T	F	S
	☐	☐	☐	☐	☐	☐	☐
	S	M	T	W	T	F	S
	☐	☐	☐	☐	☐	☐	☐
	S	M	T	W	T	F	S
	☐	☐	☐	☐	☐	☐	☐
	S	M	T	W	T	F	S
	☐	☐	☐	☐	☐	☐	☐
	S	M	T	W	T	F	S
	☐	☐	☐	☐	☐	☐	☐

FEEDING SCHEDULE

							MORNING TIME	EVENING TIME	AMOUNT
S ☐	M ☐	T ☐	W ☐	T ☐	F ☐	S ☐			
S ☐	M ☐	T ☐	W ☐	T ☐	F ☐	S ☐			
S ☐	M ☐	T ☐	W ☐	T ☐	F ☐	S ☐			
S ☐	M ☐	T ☐	W ☐	T ☐	F ☐	S ☐			
S ☐	M ☐	T ☐	W ☐	T ☐	F ☐	S ☐			
S ☐	M ☐	T ☐	W ☐	T ☐	F ☐	S ☐			
S ☐	M ☐	T ☐	W ☐	T ☐	F ☐	S ☐			
S ☐	M ☐	T ☐	W ☐	T ☐	F ☐	S ☐			
S ☐	M ☐	T ☐	W ☐	T ☐	F ☐	S ☐			
S ☐	M ☐	T ☐	W ☐	T ☐	F ☐	S ☐			
S ☐	M ☐	T ☐	W ☐	T ☐	F ☐	S ☐			
S ☐	M ☐	T ☐	W ☐	T ☐	F ☐	S ☐			
S ☐	M ☐	T ☐	W ☐	T ☐	F ☐	S ☐			
S ☐	M ☐	T ☐	W ☐	T ☐	F ☐	S ☐			
S ☐	M ☐	T ☐	W ☐	T ☐	F ☐	S ☐			
S ☐	M ☐	T ☐	W ☐	T ☐	F ☐	S ☐			
S ☐	M ☐	T ☐	W ☐	T ☐	F ☐	S ☐			
S ☐	M ☐	T ☐	W ☐	T ☐	F ☐	S ☐			
S ☐	M ☐	T ☐	W ☐	T ☐	F ☐	S ☐			
S ☐	M ☐	T ☐	W ☐	T ☐	F ☐	S ☐			

RESPONSIBILITY CHART

CHORE

	S	M	T	W	T	F	S
	☐	☐	☐	☐	☐	☐	☐
	S	M	T	W	T	F	S
	☐	☐	☐	☐	☐	☐	☐
	S	M	T	W	T	F	S
	☐	☐	☐	☐	☐	☐	☐
	S	M	T	W	T	F	S
	☐	☐	☐	☐	☐	☐	☐
	S	M	T	W	T	F	S
	☐	☐	☐	☐	☐	☐	☐
	S	M	T	W	T	F	S
	☐	☐	☐	☐	☐	☐	☐
	S	M	T	W	T	F	S
	☐	☐	☐	☐	☐	☐	☐
	S	M	T	W	T	F	S
	☐	☐	☐	☐	☐	☐	☐
	S	M	T	W	T	F	S
	☐	☐	☐	☐	☐	☐	☐
	S	M	T	W	T	F	S
	☐	☐	☐	☐	☐	☐	☐
	S	M	T	W	T	F	S
	☐	☐	☐	☐	☐	☐	☐
	S	M	T	W	T	F	S
	☐	☐	☐	☐	☐	☐	☐
	S	M	T	W	T	F	S
	☐	☐	☐	☐	☐	☐	☐
	S	M	T	W	T	F	S
	☐	☐	☐	☐	☐	☐	☐
	S	M	T	W	T	F	S
	☐	☐	☐	☐	☐	☐	☐
	S	M	T	W	T	F	S
	☐	☐	☐	☐	☐	☐	☐
	S	M	T	W	T	F	S
	☐	☐	☐	☐	☐	☐	☐
	S	M	T	W	T	F	S
	☐	☐	☐	☐	☐	☐	☐

FEEDING SCHEDULE

							MORNING TIME	EVENING TIME	AMOUNT
S	M	T	W	T	F	S			
☐	☐	☐	☐	☐	☐	☐			
S	M	T	W	T	F	S			
☐	☐	☐	☐	☐	☐	☐			
S	M	T	W	T	F	S			
☐	☐	☐	☐	☐	☐	☐			
S	M	T	W	T	F	S			
☐	☐	☐	☐	☐	☐	☐			
S	M	T	W	T	F	S			
☐	☐	☐	☐	☐	☐	☐			
S	M	T	W	T	F	S			
☐	☐	☐	☐	☐	☐	☐			
S	M	T	W	T	F	S			
☐	☐	☐	☐	☐	☐	☐			
S	M	T	W	T	F	S			
☐	☐	☐	☐	☐	☐	☐			
S	M	T	W	T	F	S			
☐	☐	☐	☐	☐	☐	☐			
S	M	T	W	T	F	S			
☐	☐	☐	☐	☐	☐	☐			
S	M	T	W	T	F	S			
☐	☐	☐	☐	☐	☐	☐			
S	M	T	W	T	F	S			
☐	☐	☐	☐	☐	☐	☐			
S	M	T	W	T	F	S			
☐	☐	☐	☐	☐	☐	☐			
S	M	T	W	T	F	S			
☐	☐	☐	☐	☐	☐	☐			
S	M	T	W	T	F	S			
☐	☐	☐	☐	☐	☐	☐			
S	M	T	W	T	F	S			
☐	☐	☐	☐	☐	☐	☐			
S	M	T	W	T	F	S			
☐	☐	☐	☐	☐	☐	☐			
S	M	T	W	T	F	S			
☐	☐	☐	☐	☐	☐	☐			
S	M	T	W	T	F	S			
☐	☐	☐	☐	☐	☐	☐			

RESPONSIBILITY CHART

CHORE

	S	M	T	W	T	F	S
	☐	☐	☐	☐	☐	☐	☐
	S	M	T	W	T	F	S
	☐	☐	☐	☐	☐	☐	☐
	S	M	T	W	T	F	S
	☐	☐	☐	☐	☐	☐	☐
	S	M	T	W	T	F	S
	☐	☐	☐	☐	☐	☐	☐
	S	M	T	W	T	F	S
	☐	☐	☐	☐	☐	☐	☐
	S	M	T	W	T	F	S
	☐	☐	☐	☐	☐	☐	☐
	S	M	T	W	T	F	S
	☐	☐	☐	☐	☐	☐	☐
	S	M	T	W	T	F	S
	☐	☐	☐	☐	☐	☐	☐
	S	M	T	W	T	F	S
	☐	☐	☐	☐	☐	☐	☐
	S	M	T	W	T	F	S
	☐	☐	☐	☐	☐	☐	☐
	S	M	T	W	T	F	S
	☐	☐	☐	☐	☐	☐	☐
	S	M	T	W	T	F	S
	☐	☐	☐	☐	☐	☐	☐
	S	M	T	W	T	F	S
	☐	☐	☐	☐	☐	☐	☐
	S	M	T	W	T	F	S
	☐	☐	☐	☐	☐	☐	☐
	S	M	T	W	T	F	S
	☐	☐	☐	☐	☐	☐	☐
	S	M	T	W	T	F	S
	☐	☐	☐	☐	☐	☐	☐
	S	M	T	W	T	F	S
	☐	☐	☐	☐	☐	☐	☐
	S	M	T	W	T	F	S
	☐	☐	☐	☐	☐	☐	☐
	S	M	T	W	T	F	S
	☐	☐	☐	☐	☐	☐	☐

FEEDING SCHEDULE

							MORNING TIME	EVENING TIME	AMOUNT
S	M	T	W	T	F	S			
☐	☐	☐	☐	☐	☐	☐			
S	M	T	W	T	F	S			
☐	☐	☐	☐	☐	☐	☐			
S	M	T	W	T	F	S			
☐	☐	☐	☐	☐	☐	☐			
S	M	T	W	T	F	S			
☐	☐	☐	☐	☐	☐	☐			
S	M	T	W	T	F	S			
☐	☐	☐	☐	☐	☐	☐			
S	M	T	W	T	F	S			
☐	☐	☐	☐	☐	☐	☐			
S	M	T	W	T	F	S			
☐	☐	☐	☐	☐	☐	☐			
S	M	T	W	T	F	S			
☐	☐	☐	☐	☐	☐	☐			
S	M	T	W	T	F	S			
☐	☐	☐	☐	☐	☐	☐			
S	M	T	W	T	F	S			
☐	☐	☐	☐	☐	☐	☐			
S	M	T	W	T	F	S			
☐	☐	☐	☐	☐	☐	☐			
S	M	T	W	T	F	S			
☐	☐	☐	☐	☐	☐	☐			
S	M	T	W	T	F	S			
☐	☐	☐	☐	☐	☐	☐			
S	M	T	W	T	F	S			
☐	☐	☐	☐	☐	☐	☐			
S	M	T	W	T	F	S			
☐	☐	☐	☐	☐	☐	☐			
S	M	T	W	T	F	S			
☐	☐	☐	☐	☐	☐	☐			
S	M	T	W	T	F	S			
☐	☐	☐	☐	☐	☐	☐			
S	M	T	W	T	F	S			
☐	☐	☐	☐	☐	☐	☐			
S	M	T	W	T	F	S			
☐	☐	☐	☐	☐	☐	☐			

RESPONSIBILITY CHART

HORE

	S	M	T	W	T	F	S
	☐	☐	☐	☐	☐	☐	☐
	S	M	T	W	T	F	S
	☐	☐	☐	☐	☐	☐	☐
	S	M	T	W	T	F	S
	☐	☐	☐	☐	☐	☐	☐
	S	M	T	W	T	F	S
	☐	☐	☐	☐	☐	☐	☐
	S	M	T	W	T	F	S
	☐	☐	☐	☐	☐	☐	☐
	S	M	T	W	T	F	S
	☐	☐	☐	☐	☐	☐	☐
	S	M	T	W	T	F	S
	☐	☐	☐	☐	☐	☐	☐
	S	M	T	W	T	F	S
	☐	☐	☐	☐	☐	☐	☐
	S	M	T	W	T	F	S
	☐	☐	☐	☐	☐	☐	☐
	S	M	T	W	T	F	S
	☐	☐	☐	☐	☐	☐	☐
	S	M	T	W	T	F	S
	☐	☐	☐	☐	☐	☐	☐
	S	M	T	W	T	F	S
	☐	☐	☐	☐	☐	☐	☐
	S	M	T	W	T	F	S
	☐	☐	☐	☐	☐	☐	☐
	S	M	T	W	T	F	S
	☐	☐	☐	☐	☐	☐	☐
	S	M	T	W	T	F	S
	☐	☐	☐	☐	☐	☐	☐
	S	M	T	W	T	F	S
	☐	☐	☐	☐	☐	☐	☐
	S	M	T	W	T	F	S
	☐	☐	☐	☐	☐	☐	☐
	S	M	T	W	T	F	S
	☐	☐	☐	☐	☐	☐	☐
	S	M	T	W	T	F	S
	☐	☐	☐	☐	☐	☐	☐

TRAINING LOG

DATE: | TIME: | HANDLER:

LOCATION: | TYPE OF TRAINING:

WEATHER: | TEMPERATURE:

TASK TYPE:

DURATION: | TREAT USED:

COMPETENCE: □ 1 □ 2 □ 3 □ 4 □ 5 □ 6 □ 7 □ 8 □ 9 □ 10

SUCCESS:

NEEDS IMPROVEMENT:

NOTES:

DATE: | TIME: | HANDLER:

LOCATION: | TYPE OF TRAINING:

WEATHER: | TEMPERATURE:

TASK TYPE:

DURATION: | TREAT USED:

COMPETENCE: □ 1 □ 2 □ 3 □ 4 □ 5 □ 6 □ 7 □ 8 □ 9 □ 1

SUCCESS:

NEEDS IMPROVEMENT:

NOTES:

TRAINING LOG

DATE: | TIME: | HANDLER:

LOCATION: | TYPE OF TRAINING:

WEATHER: | TEMPERATURE:

TASK TYPE:

DURATION: | TREAT USED:

COMPETENCE: □ 1 □ 2 □ 3 □ 4 □ 5 □ 6 □ 7 □ 8 □ 9 □ 10

SUCCESS:

NEEDS IMPROVEMENT:

NOTES:

DATE: | TIME: | HANDLER:

LOCATION: | TYPE OF TRAINING:

WEATHER: | TEMPERATURE:

TASK TYPE:

DURATION: | TREAT USED:

COMPETENCE: □ 1 □ 2 □ 3 □ 4 □ 5 □ 6 □ 7 □ 8 □ 9 □ 10

SUCCESS:

NEEDS IMPROVEMENT:

NOTES:

TRAINING LOG

DATE: TIME: HANDLER:

LOCATION: TYPE OF TRAINING:

WEATHER: TEMPERATURE:

TASK TYPE:

DURATION: TREAT USED:

COMPETENCE: □ 1   □ 2   □ 3   □ 4   □ 5   □ 6   □ 7   □ 8   □ 9   □ 10

SUCCESS:

NEEDS IMPROVEMENT:

NOTES:

DATE: TIME: HANDLER:

LOCATION: TYPE OF TRAINING:

WEATHER: TEMPERATURE:

TASK TYPE:

DURATION: TREAT USED:

COMPETENCE: □ 1   □ 2   □ 3   □ 4   □ 5   □ 6   □ 7   □ 8   □ 9   □ 10

SUCCESS:

NEEDS IMPROVEMENT:

NOTES:

TRAINING LOG

DATE: TIME: HANDLER:

LOCATION: TYPE OF TRAINING:

WEATHER: TEMPERATURE:

TASK TYPE:

DURATION: TREAT USED:

COMPETENCE: □ 1   □ 2   □ 3   □ 4   □ 5   □ 6   □ 7   □ 8   □ 9   □ 10

SUCCESS:

NEEDS IMPROVEMENT:

NOTES:

DATE: TIME: HANDLER:

LOCATION: TYPE OF TRAINING:

WEATHER: TEMPERATURE:

TASK TYPE:

DURATION: TREAT USED:

COMPETENCE: □ 1   □ 2   □ 3   □ 4   □ 5   □ 6   □ 7   □ 8   □ 9   □ 10

SUCCESS:

NEEDS IMPROVEMENT:

NOTES:

TRAINING LOG

DATE: | TIME: | HANDLER:

LOCATION: | TYPE OF TRAINING:

WEATHER: | TEMPERATURE:

TASK TYPE:

DURATION: | TREAT USED:

COMPETENCE: □ 1 □ 2 □ 3 □ 4 □ 5 □ 6 □ 7 □ 8 □ 9 □ 10

SUCCESS:

NEEDS IMPROVEMENT:

NOTES:

DATE: | TIME: | HANDLER:

LOCATION: | TYPE OF TRAINING:

WEATHER: | TEMPERATURE:

TASK TYPE:

DURATION: | TREAT USED:

COMPETENCE: □ 1 □ 2 □ 3 □ 4 □ 5 □ 6 □ 7 □ 8 □ 9 □ 1C

SUCCESS:

NEEDS IMPROVEMENT:

NOTES:

TRAINING LOG

DATE: | TIME: | HANDLER:

LOCATION: | TYPE OF TRAINING:

WEATHER: | TEMPERATURE:

TASK TYPE:

DURATION: | TREAT USED:

COMPETENCE: □ 1 □ 2 □ 3 □ 4 □ 5 □ 6 □ 7 □ 8 □ 9 □ 10

SUCCESS:

NEEDS IMPROVEMENT:

NOTES:

DATE: | TIME: | HANDLER:

LOCATION: | TYPE OF TRAINING:

WEATHER: | TEMPERATURE:

TASK TYPE:

DURATION: | TREAT USED:

COMPETENCE: □ 1 □ 2 □ 3 □ 4 □ 5 □ 6 □ 7 □ 8 □ 9 □ 10

SUCCESS:

NEEDS IMPROVEMENT:

NOTES:

TRAINING LOG

DATE: | TIME: | HANDLER:

LOCATION: | TYPE OF TRAINING:

WEATHER: | TEMPERATURE:

TASK TYPE:

DURATION: | TREAT USED:

COMPETENCE: □ 1 □ 2 □ 3 □ 4 □ 5 □ 6 □ 7 □ 8 □ 9 □10

SUCCESS:

NEEDS IMPROVEMENT:

NOTES:

DATE: | TIME: | HANDLER:

LOCATION: | TYPE OF TRAINING:

WEATHER: | TEMPERATURE:

TASK TYPE:

DURATION: | TREAT USED:

COMPETENCE: □ 1 □ 2 □ 3 □ 4 □ 5 □ 6 □ 7 □ 8 □ 9 □ 1

SUCCESS:

NEEDS IMPROVEMENT:

NOTES:

TRAINING LOG

DATE: | TIME: | HANDLER:

LOCATION: | TYPE OF TRAINING:

WEATHER: | TEMPERATURE:

TASK TYPE:

DURATION: | TREAT USED:

COMPETENCE: □ 1 □ 2 □ 3 □ 4 □ 5 □ 6 □ 7 □ 8 □ 9 □ 10

SUCCESS:

NEEDS IMPROVEMENT:

NOTES:

DATE: | TIME: | HANDLER:

LOCATION: | TYPE OF TRAINING:

WEATHER: | TEMPERATURE:

TASK TYPE:

DURATION: | TREAT USED:

COMPETENCE: □ 1 □ 2 □ 3 □ 4 □ 5 □ 6 □ 7 □ 8 □ 9 □ 10

SUCCESS:

NEEDS IMPROVEMENT:

NOTES:

TRAINING LOG

DATE: | TIME: | HANDLER:

LOCATION: | TYPE OF TRAINING:

WEATHER: | TEMPERATURE:

TASK TYPE:

DURATION: | TREAT USED:

COMPETENCE: ☐ 1 ☐ 2 ☐ 3 ☐ 4 ☐ 5 ☐ 6 ☐ 7 ☐ 8 ☐ 9 ☐ 10

SUCCESS:

NEEDS IMPROVEMENT:

NOTES:

DATE: | TIME: | HANDLER:

LOCATION: | TYPE OF TRAINING:

WEATHER: | TEMPERATURE:

TASK TYPE:

DURATION: | TREAT USED:

COMPETENCE: ☐ 1 ☐ 2 ☐ 3 ☐ 4 ☐ 5 ☐ 6 ☐ 7 ☐ 8 ☐ 9 ☐ 10

SUCCESS:

NEEDS IMPROVEMENT:

NOTES:

TRAINING LOG

DATE: TIME: HANDLER:

LOCATION: TYPE OF TRAINING:

WEATHER: TEMPERATURE:

TASK TYPE:

DURATION: TREAT USED:

COMPETENCE: □ 1   □ 2   □ 3   □ 4   □ 5   □ 6   □ 7   □ 8   □ 9   □ 10

SUCCESS:

NEEDS IMPROVEMENT:

NOTES:

DATE: TIME: HANDLER:

LOCATION: TYPE OF TRAINING:

WEATHER: TEMPERATURE:

TASK TYPE:

DURATION: TREAT USED:

COMPETENCE: □ 1   □ 2   □ 3   □ 4   □ 5   □ 6   □ 7   □ 8   □ 9   □ 10

SUCCESS:

NEEDS IMPROVEMENT:

NOTES:

TRAINING LOG

DATE: | TIME: | HANDLER:

LOCATION: | TYPE OF TRAINING:

WEATHER: | TEMPERATURE:

TASK TYPE:

DURATION: | TREAT USED:

COMPETENCE: □ 1 □ 2 □ 3 □ 4 □ 5 □ 6 □ 7 □ 8 □ 9 □ 10

SUCCESS:

NEEDS IMPROVEMENT:

NOTES:

DATE: | TIME: | HANDLER:

LOCATION: | TYPE OF TRAINING:

WEATHER: | TEMPERATURE:

TASK TYPE:

DURATION: | TREAT USED:

COMPETENCE: □ 1 □ 2 □ 3 □ 4 □ 5 □ 6 □ 7 □ 8 □ 9 □ 10

SUCCESS:

NEEDS IMPROVEMENT:

NOTES:

TRAINING LOG

DATE: | TIME: | HANDLER:

LOCATION: | TYPE OF TRAINING:

WEATHER: | TEMPERATURE:

TASK TYPE:

DURATION: | TREAT USED:

COMPETENCE: □ 1 □ 2 □ 3 □ 4 □ 5 □ 6 □ 7 □ 8 □ 9 □ 10

SUCCESS:

NEEDS IMPROVEMENT:

NOTES:

DATE: | TIME: | HANDLER:

LOCATION: | TYPE OF TRAINING:

WEATHER: | TEMPERATURE:

TASK TYPE:

DURATION: | TREAT USED:

COMPETENCE: □ 1 □ 2 □ 3 □ 4 □ 5 □ 6 □ 7 □ 8 □ 9 □ 10

SUCCESS:

NEEDS IMPROVEMENT:

NOTES:

TRAINING LOG

DATE: | TIME: | HANDLER:

LOCATION: | TYPE OF TRAINING:

WEATHER: | TEMPERATURE:

TASK TYPE:

DURATION: | TREAT USED:

COMPETENCE: ☐ 1 ☐ 2 ☐ 3 ☐ 4 ☐ 5 ☐ 6 ☐ 7 ☐ 8 ☐ 9 ☐ 10

SUCCESS:

NEEDS IMPROVEMENT:

NOTES:

DATE: | TIME: | HANDLER:

LOCATION: | TYPE OF TRAINING:

WEATHER: | TEMPERATURE:

TASK TYPE:

DURATION: | TREAT USED:

COMPETENCE: ☐ 1 ☐ 2 ☐ 3 ☐ 4 ☐ 5 ☐ 6 ☐ 7 ☐ 8 ☐ 9 ☐ 1

SUCCESS:

NEEDS IMPROVEMENT:

NOTES:

TRAINING LOG

DATE: | TIME: | HANDLER:

LOCATION: | TYPE OF TRAINING:

WEATHER: | TEMPERATURE:

TASK TYPE:

DURATION: | TREAT USED:

COMPETENCE: □ 1 □ 2 □ 3 □ 4 □ 5 □ 6 □ 7 □ 8 □ 9 □ 10

SUCCESS:

NEEDS IMPROVEMENT:

NOTES:

DATE: | TIME: | HANDLER:

LOCATION: | TYPE OF TRAINING:

WEATHER: | TEMPERATURE:

TASK TYPE:

DURATION: | TREAT USED:

COMPETENCE: □ 1 □ 2 □ 3 □ 4 □ 5 □ 6 □ 7 □ 8 □ 9 □ 10

SUCCESS:

NEEDS IMPROVEMENT:

NOTES:

TRAINING LOG

DATE: TIME: HANDLER:

LOCATION: TYPE OF TRAINING:

WEATHER: TEMPERATURE:

TASK TYPE:

DURATION: TREAT USED:

COMPETENCE: □ 1   □ 2   □ 3   □ 4   □ 5   □ 6   □ 7   □ 8   □ 9   □ 10

SUCCESS:

NEEDS IMPROVEMENT:

NOTES:

DATE: TIME: HANDLER:

LOCATION: TYPE OF TRAINING:

WEATHER: TEMPERATURE:

TASK TYPE:

DURATION: TREAT USED:

COMPETENCE: □ 1   □ 2   □ 3   □ 4   □ 5   □ 6   □ 7   □ 8   □ 9   □ 10

SUCCESS:

NEEDS IMPROVEMENT:

NOTES:

TRAINING LOG

DATE: TIME: HANDLER:

LOCATION: TYPE OF TRAINING:

WEATHER: TEMPERATURE:

TASK TYPE:

DURATION: TREAT USED:

COMPETENCE: □ 1   □ 2   □ 3   □ 4   □ 5   □ 6   □ 7   □ 8   □ 9   □ 10

SUCCESS:

NEEDS IMPROVEMENT:

NOTES:

DATE: TIME: HANDLER:

LOCATION: TYPE OF TRAINING:

WEATHER: TEMPERATURE:

TASK TYPE:

DURATION: TREAT USED:

COMPETENCE: □ 1   □ 2   □ 3   □ 4   □ 5   □ 6   □ 7   □ 8   □ 9   □ 10

SUCCESS:

NEEDS IMPROVEMENT:

NOTES:

TRAINING LOG

DATE: | TIME: | HANDLER:

LOCATION: | TYPE OF TRAINING:

WEATHER: | TEMPERATURE:

TASK TYPE:

DURATION: | TREAT USED:

COMPETENCE: ☐ 1 ☐ 2 ☐ 3 ☐ 4 ☐ 5 ☐ 6 ☐ 7 ☐ 8 ☐ 9 ☐ 10

SUCCESS:

NEEDS IMPROVEMENT:

NOTES:

DATE: | TIME: | HANDLER:

LOCATION: | TYPE OF TRAINING:

WEATHER: | TEMPERATURE:

TASK TYPE:

DURATION: | TREAT USED:

COMPETENCE: ☐ 1 ☐ 2 ☐ 3 ☐ 4 ☐ 5 ☐ 6 ☐ 7 ☐ 8 ☐ 9 ☐ 10

SUCCESS:

NEEDS IMPROVEMENT:

NOTES:

TRAINING LOG

DATE: | TIME: | HANDLER:

LOCATION: | TYPE OF TRAINING:

WEATHER: | TEMPERATURE:

TASK TYPE:

DURATION: | TREAT USED:

COMPETENCE: □ 1 □ 2 □ 3 □ 4 □ 5 □ 6 □ 7 □ 8 □ 9 □ 10

SUCCESS:

NEEDS IMPROVEMENT:

NOTES:

DATE: | TIME: | HANDLER:

LOCATION: | TYPE OF TRAINING:

WEATHER: | TEMPERATURE:

TASK TYPE:

DURATION: | TREAT USED:

COMPETENCE: □ 1 □ 2 □ 3 □ 4 □ 5 □ 6 □ 7 □ 8 □ 9 □ 10

SUCCESS:

NEEDS IMPROVEMENT:

NOTES:

TRAINING LOG

DATE: | TIME: | HANDLER:

LOCATION: | TYPE OF TRAINING:

WEATHER: | TEMPERATURE:

TASK TYPE:

DURATION: | TREAT USED:

COMPETENCE: ☐ 1 ☐ 2 ☐ 3 ☐ 4 ☐ 5 ☐ 6 ☐ 7 ☐ 8 ☐ 9 ☐ 10

SUCCESS:

NEEDS IMPROVEMENT:

NOTES:

DATE: | TIME: | HANDLER:

LOCATION: | TYPE OF TRAINING:

WEATHER: | TEMPERATURE:

TASK TYPE:

DURATION: | TREAT USED:

COMPETENCE: ☐ 1 ☐ 2 ☐ 3 ☐ 4 ☐ 5 ☐ 6 ☐ 7 ☐ 8 ☐ 9 ☐ 1

SUCCESS:

NEEDS IMPROVEMENT:

NOTES:

TRAINING LOG

DATE: TIME: HANDLER:

LOCATION: TYPE OF TRAINING:

WEATHER: TEMPERATURE:

TASK TYPE:

DURATION: TREAT USED:

COMPETENCE: □ 1   □ 2   □ 3   □ 4   □ 5   □ 6   □ 7   □ 8   □ 9   □ 10

SUCCESS:

NEEDS IMPROVEMENT:

NOTES:

DATE: TIME: HANDLER:

LOCATION: TYPE OF TRAINING:

WEATHER: TEMPERATURE:

TASK TYPE:

DURATION: TREAT USED:

COMPETENCE: □ 1   □ 2   □ 3   □ 4   □ 5   □ 6   □ 7   □ 8   □ 9   □ 10

SUCCESS:

NEEDS IMPROVEMENT:

NOTES:

TRAINING LOG

DATE: | TIME: | HANDLER:

LOCATION: | TYPE OF TRAINING:

WEATHER: | TEMPERATURE:

TASK TYPE:

DURATION: | TREAT USED:

COMPETENCE: □ 1 □ 2 □ 3 □ 4 □ 5 □ 6 □ 7 □ 8 □ 9 □ 10

SUCCESS:

NEEDS IMPROVEMENT:

NOTES:

DATE: | TIME: | HANDLER:

LOCATION: | TYPE OF TRAINING:

WEATHER: | TEMPERATURE:

TASK TYPE:

DURATION: | TREAT USED:

COMPETENCE: □ 1 □ 2 □ 3 □ 4 □ 5 □ 6 □ 7 □ 8 □ 9 □ 10

SUCCESS:

NEEDS IMPROVEMENT:

NOTES:

TRAINING LOG

DATE: | TIME: | HANDLER:

LOCATION: | TYPE OF TRAINING:

WEATHER: | TEMPERATURE:

TASK TYPE:

DURATION: | TREAT USED:

COMPETENCE: □ 1 □ 2 □ 3 □ 4 □ 5 □ 6 □ 7 □ 8 □ 9 □ 10

SUCCESS:

NEEDS IMPROVEMENT:

NOTES:

DATE: | TIME: | HANDLER:

LOCATION: | TYPE OF TRAINING:

WEATHER: | TEMPERATURE:

TASK TYPE:

DURATION: | TREAT USED:

COMPETENCE: □ 1 □ 2 □ 3 □ 4 □ 5 □ 6 □ 7 □ 8 □ 9 □ 10

SUCCESS:

NEEDS IMPROVEMENT:

NOTES:

TRAINING LOG

DATE: | TIME: | HANDLER:

LOCATION: | TYPE OF TRAINING:

WEATHER: | TEMPERATURE:

TASK TYPE:

DURATION: | TREAT USED:

COMPETENCE: ☐ 1 ☐ 2 ☐ 3 ☐ 4 ☐ 5 ☐ 6 ☐ 7 ☐ 8 ☐ 9 ☐ 10

SUCCESS:

NEEDS IMPROVEMENT:

NOTES:

DATE: | TIME: | HANDLER:

LOCATION: | TYPE OF TRAINING:

WEATHER: | TEMPERATURE:

TASK TYPE:

DURATION: | TREAT USED:

COMPETENCE: ☐ 1 ☐ 2 ☐ 3 ☐ 4 ☐ 5 ☐ 6 ☐ 7 ☐ 8 ☐ 9 ☐ 10

SUCCESS:

NEEDS IMPROVEMENT:

NOTES:

TRAINING LOG

DATE: | TIME: | HANDLER:

LOCATION: | TYPE OF TRAINING:

WEATHER: | TEMPERATURE:

TASK TYPE:

DURATION: | TREAT USED:

COMPETENCE: □ 1 □ 2 □ 3 □ 4 □ 5 □ 6 □ 7 □ 8 □ 9 □ 10

SUCCESS:

NEEDS IMPROVEMENT:

NOTES:

DATE: | TIME: | HANDLER:

LOCATION: | TYPE OF TRAINING:

WEATHER: | TEMPERATURE:

TASK TYPE:

DURATION: | TREAT USED:

COMPETENCE: □ 1 □ 2 □ 3 □ 4 □ 5 □ 6 □ 7 □ 8 □ 9 □ 10

SUCCESS:

NEEDS IMPROVEMENT:

NOTES:

TRAINING LOG

DATE: TIME: HANDLER:

LOCATION: TYPE OF TRAINING:

WEATHER: TEMPERATURE:

TASK TYPE:

DURATION: TREAT USED:

COMPETENCE: □ 1   □ 2   □ 3   □ 4   □ 5   □ 6   □ 7   □ 8   □ 9   □ 10

SUCCESS:

NEEDS IMPROVEMENT:

NOTES:

DATE: TIME: HANDLER:

LOCATION: TYPE OF TRAINING:

WEATHER: TEMPERATURE:

TASK TYPE:

DURATION: TREAT USED:

COMPETENCE: □ 1   □ 2   □ 3   □ 4   □ 5   □ 6   □ 7   □ 8   □ 9   □ 1

SUCCESS:

NEEDS IMPROVEMENT:

NOTES:

TRAINING LOG

DATE: | TIME: | HANDLER:

LOCATION: | TYPE OF TRAINING:

WEATHER: | TEMPERATURE:

TASK TYPE:

DURATION: | TREAT USED:

COMPETENCE: □ 1 □ 2 □ 3 □ 4 □ 5 □ 6 □ 7 □ 8 □ 9 □ 10

SUCCESS:

NEEDS IMPROVEMENT:

NOTES:

DATE: | TIME: | HANDLER:

LOCATION: | TYPE OF TRAINING:

WEATHER: | TEMPERATURE:

TASK TYPE:

DURATION: | TREAT USED:

COMPETENCE: □ 1 □ 2 □ 3 □ 4 □ 5 □ 6 □ 7 □ 8 □ 9 □ 10

SUCCESS:

NEEDS IMPROVEMENT:

NOTES:

TRAINING LOG

DATE: | TIME: | HANDLER:

LOCATION: | TYPE OF TRAINING:

WEATHER: | TEMPERATURE:

TASK TYPE:

DURATION: | TREAT USED:

COMPETENCE: □ 1 □ 2 □ 3 □ 4 □ 5 □ 6 □ 7 □ 8 □ 9 □ 10

SUCCESS:

NEEDS IMPROVEMENT:

NOTES:

DATE: | TIME: | HANDLER:

LOCATION: | TYPE OF TRAINING:

WEATHER: | TEMPERATURE:

TASK TYPE:

DURATION: | TREAT USED:

COMPETENCE: □ 1 □ 2 □ 3 □ 4 □ 5 □ 6 □ 7 □ 8 □ 9 □ 10

SUCCESS:

NEEDS IMPROVEMENT:

NOTES:

TRAINING LOG

DATE: TIME: HANDLER:

LOCATION: TYPE OF TRAINING:

WEATHER: TEMPERATURE:

TASK TYPE:

DURATION: TREAT USED:

COMPETENCE: □ 1   □ 2   □ 3   □ 4   □ 5   □ 6   □ 7   □ 8   □ 9   □ 10

SUCCESS:

NEEDS IMPROVEMENT:

NOTES:

DATE: TIME: HANDLER:

LOCATION: TYPE OF TRAINING:

WEATHER: TEMPERATURE:

TASK TYPE:

DURATION: TREAT USED:

COMPETENCE: □ 1   □ 2   □ 3   □ 4   □ 5   □ 6   □ 7   □ 8   □ 9   □ 10

SUCCESS:

NEEDS IMPROVEMENT:

NOTES:

TRAINING LOG

DATE: | TIME: | HANDLER:

LOCATION: | TYPE OF TRAINING:

WEATHER: | TEMPERATURE:

TASK TYPE:

DURATION: | TREAT USED:

COMPETENCE: ☐ 1 ☐ 2 ☐ 3 ☐ 4 ☐ 5 ☐ 6 ☐ 7 ☐ 8 ☐ 9 ☐ 10

SUCCESS:

NEEDS IMPROVEMENT:

NOTES:

DATE: | TIME: | HANDLER:

LOCATION: | TYPE OF TRAINING:

WEATHER: | TEMPERATURE:

TASK TYPE:

DURATION: | TREAT USED:

COMPETENCE: ☐ 1 ☐ 2 ☐ 3 ☐ 4 ☐ 5 ☐ 6 ☐ 7 ☐ 8 ☐ 9 ☐ 10

SUCCESS:

NEEDS IMPROVEMENT:

NOTES:

TRAINING LOG

DATE: | TIME: | HANDLER:

LOCATION: | TYPE OF TRAINING:

WEATHER: | TEMPERATURE:

TASK TYPE:

DURATION: | TREAT USED:

COMPETENCE: □ 1 □ 2 □ 3 □ 4 □ 5 □ 6 □ 7 □ 8 □ 9 □ 10

SUCCESS:

NEEDS IMPROVEMENT:

NOTES:

DATE: | TIME: | HANDLER:

LOCATION: | TYPE OF TRAINING:

WEATHER: | TEMPERATURE:

TASK TYPE:

DURATION: | TREAT USED:

COMPETENCE: □ 1 □ 2 □ 3 □ 4 □ 5 □ 6 □ 7 □ 8 □ 9 □ 10

SUCCESS:

NEEDS IMPROVEMENT:

NOTES:

TRAINING LOG

DATE: | TIME: | HANDLER:

LOCATION: | TYPE OF TRAINING:

WEATHER: | TEMPERATURE:

TASK TYPE:

DURATION: | TREAT USED:

COMPETENCE: ☐ 1 ☐ 2 ☐ 3 ☐ 4 ☐ 5 ☐ 6 ☐ 7 ☐ 8 ☐ 9 ☐10

SUCCESS:

NEEDS IMPROVEMENT:

NOTES:

DATE: | TIME: | HANDLER:

LOCATION: | TYPE OF TRAINING:

WEATHER: | TEMPERATURE:

TASK TYPE:

DURATION: | TREAT USED:

COMPETENCE: ☐ 1 ☐ 2 ☐ 3 ☐ 4 ☐ 5 ☐ 6 ☐ 7 ☐ 8 ☐ 9 ☐ 1

SUCCESS:

NEEDS IMPROVEMENT:

NOTES:

TRAINING LOG

DATE: TIME: HANDLER:

LOCATION: TYPE OF TRAINING:

WEATHER: TEMPERATURE:

TASK TYPE:

DURATION: TREAT USED:

COMPETENCE: □ 1   □ 2   □ 3   □ 4   □ 5   □ 6   □ 7   □ 8   □ 9   □ 10

SUCCESS:

NEEDS IMPROVEMENT:

NOTES:

DATE: TIME: HANDLER:

LOCATION: TYPE OF TRAINING:

WEATHER: TEMPERATURE:

TASK TYPE:

DURATION: TREAT USED:

COMPETENCE: □ 1   □ 2   □ 3   □ 4   □ 5   □ 6   □ 7   □ 8   □ 9   □ 10

SUCCESS:

NEEDS IMPROVEMENT:

NOTES:

TRAINING LOG

DATE: | TIME: | HANDLER:

LOCATION: | TYPE OF TRAINING:

WEATHER: | TEMPERATURE:

TASK TYPE:

DURATION: | TREAT USED:

COMPETENCE: □ 1 □ 2 □ 3 □ 4 □ 5 □ 6 □ 7 □ 8 □ 9 □ 10

SUCCESS:

NEEDS IMPROVEMENT:

NOTES:

DATE: | TIME: | HANDLER:

LOCATION: | TYPE OF TRAINING:

WEATHER: | TEMPERATURE:

TASK TYPE:

DURATION: | TREAT USED:

COMPETENCE: □ 1 □ 2 □ 3 □ 4 □ 5 □ 6 □ 7 □ 8 □ 9 □ 10

SUCCESS:

NEEDS IMPROVEMENT:

NOTES:

TRAINING LOG

DATE: | TIME: | HANDLER:

LOCATION: | TYPE OF TRAINING:

WEATHER: | TEMPERATURE:

TASK TYPE:

DURATION: | TREAT USED:

COMPETENCE: □ 1 □ 2 □ 3 □ 4 □ 5 □ 6 □ 7 □ 8 □ 9 □ 10

SUCCESS:

NEEDS IMPROVEMENT:

NOTES:

DATE: | TIME: | HANDLER:

LOCATION: | TYPE OF TRAINING:

WEATHER: | TEMPERATURE:

TASK TYPE:

DURATION: | TREAT USED:

COMPETENCE: □ 1 □ 2 □ 3 □ 4 □ 5 □ 6 □ 7 □ 8 □ 9 □ 10

SUCCESS:

NEEDS IMPROVEMENT:

NOTES:

TRAINING LOG

DATE: | TIME: | HANDLER:

LOCATION: | TYPE OF TRAINING:

WEATHER: | TEMPERATURE:

TASK TYPE:

DURATION: | TREAT USED:

COMPETENCE: □ 1 □ 2 □ 3 □ 4 □ 5 □ 6 □ 7 □ 8 □ 9 □ 10

SUCCESS:

NEEDS IMPROVEMENT:

NOTES:

DATE: | TIME: | HANDLER:

LOCATION: | TYPE OF TRAINING:

WEATHER: | TEMPERATURE:

TASK TYPE:

DURATION: | TREAT USED:

COMPETENCE: □ 1 □ 2 □ 3 □ 4 □ 5 □ 6 □ 7 □ 8 □ 9 □ 1(

SUCCESS:

NEEDS IMPROVEMENT:

NOTES:

TRAINING LOG

DATE: | TIME: | HANDLER:

LOCATION: | TYPE OF TRAINING:

WEATHER: | TEMPERATURE:

TASK TYPE:

DURATION: | TREAT USED:

COMPETENCE: □ 1 □ 2 □ 3 □ 4 □ 5 □ 6 □ 7 □ 8 □ 9 □ 10

SUCCESS:

NEEDS IMPROVEMENT:

NOTES:

DATE: | TIME: | HANDLER:

LOCATION: | TYPE OF TRAINING:

WEATHER: | TEMPERATURE:

TASK TYPE:

DURATION: | TREAT USED:

COMPETENCE: □ 1 □ 2 □ 3 □ 4 □ 5 □ 6 □ 7 □ 8 □ 9 □ 10

SUCCESS:

NEEDS IMPROVEMENT:

NOTES:

TRAINING LOG

DATE: | TIME: | HANDLER:

LOCATION: | TYPE OF TRAINING:

WEATHER: | TEMPERATURE:

TASK TYPE:

DURATION: | TREAT USED:

COMPETENCE: □ 1 □ 2 □ 3 □ 4 □ 5 □ 6 □ 7 □ 8 □ 9 □ 10

SUCCESS:

NEEDS IMPROVEMENT:

NOTES:

DATE: | TIME: | HANDLER:

LOCATION: | TYPE OF TRAINING:

WEATHER: | TEMPERATURE:

TASK TYPE:

DURATION: | TREAT USED:

COMPETENCE: □ 1 □ 2 □ 3 □ 4 □ 5 □ 6 □ 7 □ 8 □ 9 □ 1

SUCCESS:

NEEDS IMPROVEMENT:

NOTES:

TRAINING LOG

DATE: TIME: HANDLER:

LOCATION: TYPE OF TRAINING:

WEATHER: TEMPERATURE:

TASK TYPE:

DURATION: TREAT USED:

COMPETENCE: □ 1   □ 2   □ 3   □ 4   □ 5   □ 6   □ 7   □ 8   □ 9   □ 10

SUCCESS:

NEEDS IMPROVEMENT:

NOTES:

DATE: TIME: HANDLER:

LOCATION: TYPE OF TRAINING:

WEATHER: TEMPERATURE:

TASK TYPE:

DURATION: TREAT USED:

COMPETENCE: □ 1   □ 2   □ 3   □ 4   □ 5   □ 6   □ 7   □ 8   □ 9   □ 10

SUCCESS:

NEEDS IMPROVEMENT:

NOTES:

TRAINING LOG

DATE: | TIME: | HANDLER:

LOCATION: | TYPE OF TRAINING:

WEATHER: | TEMPERATURE:

TASK TYPE:

DURATION: | TREAT USED:

COMPETENCE: □ 1 □ 2 □ 3 □ 4 □ 5 □ 6 □ 7 □ 8 □ 9 □ 10

SUCCESS:

NEEDS IMPROVEMENT:

NOTES:

DATE: | TIME: | HANDLER:

LOCATION: | TYPE OF TRAINING:

WEATHER: | TEMPERATURE:

TASK TYPE:

DURATION: | TREAT USED:

COMPETENCE: □ 1 □ 2 □ 3 □ 4 □ 5 □ 6 □ 7 □ 8 □ 9 □ 10

SUCCESS:

NEEDS IMPROVEMENT:

NOTES:

TRAINING LOG

DATE: | TIME: | HANDLER:

LOCATION: | TYPE OF TRAINING:

WEATHER: | TEMPERATURE:

TASK TYPE:

DURATION: | TREAT USED:

COMPETENCE: □ 1 □ 2 □ 3 □ 4 □ 5 □ 6 □ 7 □ 8 □ 9 □ 10

SUCCESS:

NEEDS IMPROVEMENT:

NOTES:

DATE: | TIME: | HANDLER:

LOCATION: | TYPE OF TRAINING:

WEATHER: | TEMPERATURE:

TASK TYPE:

DURATION: | TREAT USED:

COMPETENCE: □ 1 □ 2 □ 3 □ 4 □ 5 □ 6 □ 7 □ 8 □ 9 □ 10

SUCCESS:

NEEDS IMPROVEMENT:

NOTES:

TRAINING LOG

DATE: TIME: HANDLER:

LOCATION: TYPE OF TRAINING:

WEATHER: TEMPERATURE:

TASK TYPE:

DURATION: TREAT USED:

COMPETENCE: □ 1   □ 2   □ 3   □ 4   □ 5   □ 6   □ 7   □ 8   □ 9   □ 10

SUCCESS:

NEEDS IMPROVEMENT:

NOTES:

DATE: TIME: HANDLER:

LOCATION: TYPE OF TRAINING:

WEATHER: TEMPERATURE:

TASK TYPE:

DURATION: TREAT USED:

COMPETENCE: □ 1   □ 2   □ 3   □ 4   □ 5   □ 6   □ 7   □ 8   □ 9   □ 10

SUCCESS:

NEEDS IMPROVEMENT:

NOTES:

TRAINING LOG

DATE: | TIME: | HANDLER:

LOCATION: | TYPE OF TRAINING:

WEATHER: | TEMPERATURE:

TASK TYPE:

DURATION: | TREAT USED:

COMPETENCE: □ 1 □ 2 □ 3 □ 4 □ 5 □ 6 □ 7 □ 8 □ 9 □ 10

SUCCESS:

NEEDS IMPROVEMENT:

NOTES:

DATE: | TIME: | HANDLER:

LOCATION: | TYPE OF TRAINING:

WEATHER: | TEMPERATURE:

TASK TYPE:

DURATION: | TREAT USED:

COMPETENCE: □ 1 □ 2 □ 3 □ 4 □ 5 □ 6 □ 7 □ 8 □ 9 □ 10

SUCCESS:

NEEDS IMPROVEMENT:

NOTES:

TRAINING LOG

DATE: | TIME: | HANDLER:

LOCATION: | TYPE OF TRAINING:

WEATHER: | TEMPERATURE:

TASK TYPE:

DURATION: | TREAT USED:

COMPETENCE: ☐ 1 ☐ 2 ☐ 3 ☐ 4 ☐ 5 ☐ 6 ☐ 7 ☐ 8 ☐ 9 ☐ 10

SUCCESS:

NEEDS IMPROVEMENT:

NOTES:

DATE: | TIME: | HANDLER:

LOCATION: | TYPE OF TRAINING:

WEATHER: | TEMPERATURE:

TASK TYPE:

DURATION: | TREAT USED:

COMPETENCE: ☐ 1 ☐ 2 ☐ 3 ☐ 4 ☐ 5 ☐ 6 ☐ 7 ☐ 8 ☐ 9 ☐ 1

SUCCESS:

NEEDS IMPROVEMENT:

NOTES:

TRAINING LOG

DATE: | TIME: | HANDLER:

LOCATION: | TYPE OF TRAINING:

WEATHER: | TEMPERATURE:

TASK TYPE:

DURATION: | TREAT USED:

COMPETENCE: □ 1 □ 2 □ 3 □ 4 □ 5 □ 6 □ 7 □ 8 □ 9 □ 10

SUCCESS:

NEEDS IMPROVEMENT:

NOTES:

DATE: | TIME: | HANDLER:

LOCATION: | TYPE OF TRAINING:

WEATHER: | TEMPERATURE:

TASK TYPE:

DURATION: | TREAT USED:

COMPETENCE: □ 1 □ 2 □ 3 □ 4 □ 5 □ 6 □ 7 □ 8 □ 9 □ 10

SUCCESS:

NEEDS IMPROVEMENT:

NOTES:

TRAINING LOG

DATE: TIME: HANDLER:

LOCATION: TYPE OF TRAINING:

WEATHER: TEMPERATURE:

TASK TYPE:

DURATION: TREAT USED:

COMPETENCE: □ 1   □ 2   □ 3   □ 4   □ 5   □ 6   □ 7   □ 8   □ 9   □ 10

SUCCESS:

NEEDS IMPROVEMENT:

NOTES:

DATE: TIME: HANDLER:

LOCATION: TYPE OF TRAINING:

WEATHER: TEMPERATURE:

TASK TYPE:

DURATION: TREAT USED:

COMPETENCE: □ 1   □ 2   □ 3   □ 4   □ 5   □ 6   □ 7   □ 8   □ 9   □ 1(

SUCCESS:

NEEDS IMPROVEMENT:

NOTES:

TRAINING LOG

DATE: | TIME: | HANDLER:

LOCATION: | TYPE OF TRAINING:

WEATHER: | TEMPERATURE:

TASK TYPE:

DURATION: | TREAT USED:

COMPETENCE: □ 1   □ 2   □ 3   □ 4   □ 5   □ 6   □ 7   □ 8   □ 9   □ 10

SUCCESS:

NEEDS IMPROVEMENT:

NOTES:

DATE: | TIME: | HANDLER:

LOCATION: | TYPE OF TRAINING:

WEATHER: | TEMPERATURE:

TASK TYPE:

DURATION: | TREAT USED:

COMPETENCE: □ 1   □ 2   □ 3   □ 4   □ 5   □ 6   □ 7   □ 8   □ 9   □ 10

SUCCESS:

NEEDS IMPROVEMENT:

NOTES:

TRAINING LOG

DATE: | TIME: | HANDLER:

LOCATION: | TYPE OF TRAINING:

WEATHER: | TEMPERATURE:

TASK TYPE:

DURATION: | TREAT USED:

COMPETENCE: □ 1 □ 2 □ 3 □ 4 □ 5 □ 6 □ 7 □ 8 □ 9 □ 10

SUCCESS:

NEEDS IMPROVEMENT:

NOTES:

DATE: | TIME: | HANDLER:

LOCATION: | TYPE OF TRAINING:

WEATHER: | TEMPERATURE:

TASK TYPE:

DURATION: | TREAT USED:

COMPETENCE: □ 1 □ 2 □ 3 □ 4 □ 5 □ 6 □ 7 □ 8 □ 9 □ 10

SUCCESS:

NEEDS IMPROVEMENT:

NOTES:

TRAINING LOG

DATE: | TIME: | HANDLER:

LOCATION: | TYPE OF TRAINING:

WEATHER: | TEMPERATURE:

TASK TYPE:

DURATION: | TREAT USED:

COMPETENCE: □ 1 □ 2 □ 3 □ 4 □ 5 □ 6 □ 7 □ 8 □ 9 □ 10

SUCCESS:

NEEDS IMPROVEMENT:

NOTES:

DATE: | TIME: | HANDLER:

LOCATION: | TYPE OF TRAINING:

WEATHER: | TEMPERATURE:

TASK TYPE:

DURATION: | TREAT USED:

COMPETENCE: □ 1 □ 2 □ 3 □ 4 □ 5 □ 6 □ 7 □ 8 □ 9 □ 10

SUCCESS:

NEEDS IMPROVEMENT:

NOTES:

TRAINING LOG

DATE: TIME: HANDLER:

LOCATION: TYPE OF TRAINING:

WEATHER: TEMPERATURE:

TASK TYPE:

DURATION: TREAT USED:

COMPETENCE: □ 1   □ 2   □ 3   □ 4   □ 5   □ 6   □ 7   □ 8   □ 9   □ 10

SUCCESS:

NEEDS IMPROVEMENT:

NOTES:

DATE: TIME: HANDLER:

LOCATION: TYPE OF TRAINING:

WEATHER: TEMPERATURE:

TASK TYPE:

DURATION: TREAT USED:

COMPETENCE: □ 1   □ 2   □ 3   □ 4   □ 5   □ 6   □ 7   □ 8   □ 9   □ 1

SUCCESS:

NEEDS IMPROVEMENT:

NOTES:

TRAINING LOG

DATE: | TIME: | HANDLER:

LOCATION: | TYPE OF TRAINING:

WEATHER: | TEMPERATURE:

TASK TYPE:

DURATION: | TREAT USED:

COMPETENCE: □ 1 □ 2 □ 3 □ 4 □ 5 □ 6 □ 7 □ 8 □ 9 □ 10

SUCCESS:

NEEDS IMPROVEMENT:

NOTES:

DATE: | TIME: | HANDLER:

LOCATION: | TYPE OF TRAINING:

WEATHER: | TEMPERATURE:

TASK TYPE:

DURATION: | TREAT USED:

COMPETENCE: □ 1 □ 2 □ 3 □ 4 □ 5 □ 6 □ 7 □ 8 □ 9 □ 10

SUCCESS:

NEEDS IMPROVEMENT:

NOTES:

TRAINING LOG

DATE: | TIME: | HANDLER:

LOCATION: | TYPE OF TRAINING:

WEATHER: | TEMPERATURE:

TASK TYPE:

DURATION: | TREAT USED:

COMPETENCE: □ 1 □ 2 □ 3 □ 4 □ 5 □ 6 □ 7 □ 8 □ 9 □ 10

SUCCESS:

NEEDS IMPROVEMENT:

NOTES:

DATE: | TIME: | HANDLER:

LOCATION: | TYPE OF TRAINING:

WEATHER: | TEMPERATURE:

TASK TYPE:

DURATION: | TREAT USED:

COMPETENCE: □ 1 □ 2 □ 3 □ 4 □ 5 □ 6 □ 7 □ 8 □ 9 □ 10

SUCCESS:

NEEDS IMPROVEMENT:

NOTES:

TRAINING LOG

DATE: TIME: HANDLER:

LOCATION: TYPE OF TRAINING:

WEATHER: TEMPERATURE:

TASK TYPE:

DURATION: TREAT USED:

COMPETENCE: □ 1   □ 2   □ 3   □ 4   □ 5   □ 6   □ 7   □ 8   □ 9   □ 10

SUCCESS:

NEEDS IMPROVEMENT:

NOTES:

DATE: TIME: HANDLER:

LOCATION: TYPE OF TRAINING:

WEATHER: TEMPERATURE:

TASK TYPE:

DURATION: TREAT USED:

COMPETENCE: □ 1   □ 2   □ 3   □ 4   □ 5   □ 6   □ 7   □ 8   □ 9   □ 10

SUCCESS:

NEEDS IMPROVEMENT:

NOTES:

TRAINING LOG

DATE: TIME: HANDLER:

LOCATION: TYPE OF TRAINING:

WEATHER: TEMPERATURE:

TASK TYPE:

DURATION: TREAT USED:

COMPETENCE: □ 1   □ 2   □ 3   □ 4   □ 5   □ 6   □ 7   □ 8   □ 9   □ 10

SUCCESS:

NEEDS IMPROVEMENT:

NOTES:

DATE: TIME: HANDLER:

LOCATION: TYPE OF TRAINING:

WEATHER: TEMPERATURE:

TASK TYPE:

DURATION: TREAT USED:

COMPETENCE: □ 1   □ 2   □ 3   □ 4   □ 5   □ 6   □ 7   □ 8   □ 9   □ 10

SUCCESS:

NEEDS IMPROVEMENT:

NOTES:

TRAINING LOG

DATE: | TIME: | HANDLER:

LOCATION: | TYPE OF TRAINING:

WEATHER: | TEMPERATURE:

TASK TYPE:

DURATION: | TREAT USED:

COMPETENCE: □ 1 □ 2 □ 3 □ 4 □ 5 □ 6 □ 7 □ 8 □ 9 □ 10

SUCCESS:

NEEDS IMPROVEMENT:

NOTES:

DATE: | TIME: | HANDLER:

LOCATION: | TYPE OF TRAINING:

WEATHER: | TEMPERATURE:

TASK TYPE:

DURATION: | TREAT USED:

COMPETENCE: □ 1 □ 2 □ 3 □ 4 □ 5 □ 6 □ 7 □ 8 □ 9 □ 10

SUCCESS:

NEEDS IMPROVEMENT:

NOTES:

TRAINING LOG

DATE: | TIME: | HANDLER:

LOCATION: | TYPE OF TRAINING:

WEATHER: | TEMPERATURE:

TASK TYPE:

DURATION: | TREAT USED:

COMPETENCE: □ 1 □ 2 □ 3 □ 4 □ 5 □ 6 □ 7 □ 8 □ 9 □ 10

SUCCESS:

NEEDS IMPROVEMENT:

NOTES:

DATE: | TIME: | HANDLER:

LOCATION: | TYPE OF TRAINING:

WEATHER: | TEMPERATURE:

TASK TYPE:

DURATION: | TREAT USED:

COMPETENCE: □ 1 □ 2 □ 3 □ 4 □ 5 □ 6 □ 7 □ 8 □ 9 □ 1

SUCCESS:

NEEDS IMPROVEMENT:

NOTES:

TRAINING LOG

DATE: | TIME: | HANDLER:

LOCATION: | TYPE OF TRAINING:

WEATHER: | TEMPERATURE:

TASK TYPE:

DURATION: | TREAT USED:

COMPETENCE: □ 1 □ 2 □ 3 □ 4 □ 5 □ 6 □ 7 □ 8 □ 9 □ 10

SUCCESS:

NEEDS IMPROVEMENT:

NOTES:

DATE: | TIME: | HANDLER:

LOCATION: | TYPE OF TRAINING:

WEATHER: | TEMPERATURE:

TASK TYPE:

DURATION: | TREAT USED:

COMPETENCE: □ 1 □ 2 □ 3 □ 4 □ 5 □ 6 □ 7 □ 8 □ 9 □ 10

SUCCESS:

NEEDS IMPROVEMENT:

NOTES:

TRAINING LOG

DATE: TIME: HANDLER:

LOCATION: TYPE OF TRAINING:

WEATHER: TEMPERATURE:

TASK TYPE:

DURATION: TREAT USED:

COMPETENCE: □ 1   □ 2   □ 3   □ 4   □ 5   □ 6   □ 7   □ 8   □ 9   □ 10

SUCCESS:

NEEDS IMPROVEMENT:

NOTES:

DATE: TIME: HANDLER:

LOCATION: TYPE OF TRAINING:

WEATHER: TEMPERATURE:

TASK TYPE:

DURATION: TREAT USED:

COMPETENCE: □ 1   □ 2   □ 3   □ 4   □ 5   □ 6   □ 7   □ 8   □ 9   □ 10

SUCCESS:

NEEDS IMPROVEMENT:

NOTES:

TRAINING LOG

DATE: | TIME: | HANDLER:

LOCATION: | TYPE OF TRAINING:

WEATHER: | TEMPERATURE:

TASK TYPE:

DURATION: | TREAT USED:

COMPETENCE: □ 1 □ 2 □ 3 □ 4 □ 5 □ 6 □ 7 □ 8 □ 9 □ 10

SUCCESS:

NEEDS IMPROVEMENT:

NOTES:

DATE: | TIME: | HANDLER:

LOCATION: | TYPE OF TRAINING:

WEATHER: | TEMPERATURE:

TASK TYPE:

DURATION: | TREAT USED:

COMPETENCE: □ 1 □ 2 □ 3 □ 4 □ 5 □ 6 □ 7 □ 8 □ 9 □ 10

SUCCESS:

NEEDS IMPROVEMENT:

NOTES:

TRAINING LOG

DATE: TIME: HANDLER:

LOCATION: TYPE OF TRAINING:

WEATHER: TEMPERATURE:

TASK TYPE:

DURATION: TREAT USED:

COMPETENCE: □ 1   □ 2   □ 3   □ 4   □ 5   □ 6   □ 7   □ 8   □ 9   □ 10

SUCCESS:

NEEDS IMPROVEMENT:

NOTES:

DATE: TIME: HANDLER:

LOCATION: TYPE OF TRAINING:

WEATHER: TEMPERATURE:

TASK TYPE:

DURATION: TREAT USED:

COMPETENCE: □ 1   □ 2   □ 3   □ 4   □ 5   □ 6   □ 7   □ 8   □ 9   □ 1(

SUCCESS:

NEEDS IMPROVEMENT:

NOTES:

TRAINING LOG

DATE: _____ TIME: _____ HANDLER: _____

LOCATION: _____ TYPE OF TRAINING: _____

WEATHER: _____ TEMPERATURE: _____

TASK TYPE: _____

DURATION: _____ TREAT USED: _____

COMPETENCE: □ 1 □ 2 □ 3 □ 4 □ 5 □ 6 □ 7 □ 8 □ 9 □ 10

SUCCESS: _____

NEEDS IMPROVEMENT: _____

NOTES: _____

DATE: _____ TIME: _____ HANDLER: _____

LOCATION: _____ TYPE OF TRAINING: _____

WEATHER: _____ TEMPERATURE: _____

TASK TYPE: _____

DURATION: _____ TREAT USED: _____

COMPETENCE: □ 1 □ 2 □ 3 □ 4 □ 5 □ 6 □ 7 □ 8 □ 9 □ 10

SUCCESS: _____

NEEDS IMPROVEMENT: _____

NOTES: _____

TRAINING LOG

DATE: TIME: HANDLER:

LOCATION: TYPE OF TRAINING:

WEATHER: TEMPERATURE:

TASK TYPE:

DURATION: TREAT USED:

COMPETENCE: □ 1   □ 2   □ 3   □ 4   □ 5   □ 6   □ 7   □ 8   □ 9   □ 10

SUCCESS:

NEEDS IMPROVEMENT:

NOTES:

DATE: TIME: HANDLER:

LOCATION: TYPE OF TRAINING:

WEATHER: TEMPERATURE:

TASK TYPE:

DURATION: TREAT USED:

COMPETENCE: □ 1   □ 2   □ 3   □ 4   □ 5   □ 6   □ 7   □ 8   □ 9   □ 1

SUCCESS:

NEEDS IMPROVEMENT:

NOTES:

TRAINING LOG

DATE: TIME: HANDLER:

LOCATION: TYPE OF TRAINING:

WEATHER: TEMPERATURE:

TASK TYPE:

DURATION: TREAT USED:

COMPETENCE: □ 1   □ 2   □ 3   □ 4   □ 5   □ 6   □ 7   □ 8   □ 9   □ 10

SUCCESS:

NEEDS IMPROVEMENT:

NOTES:

DATE: TIME: HANDLER:

LOCATION: TYPE OF TRAINING:

WEATHER: TEMPERATURE:

TASK TYPE:

DURATION: TREAT USED:

COMPETENCE: □ 1   □ 2   □ 3   □ 4   □ 5   □ 6   □ 7   □ 8   □ 9   □ 10

SUCCESS:

NEEDS IMPROVEMENT:

NOTES:

TRAINING LOG

DATE: | TIME: | HANDLER:

LOCATION: | TYPE OF TRAINING:

WEATHER: | TEMPERATURE:

TASK TYPE:

DURATION: | TREAT USED:

COMPETENCE: ☐ 1 ☐ 2 ☐ 3 ☐ 4 ☐ 5 ☐ 6 ☐ 7 ☐ 8 ☐ 9 ☐ 10

SUCCESS:

NEEDS IMPROVEMENT:

NOTES:

DATE: | TIME: | HANDLER:

LOCATION: | TYPE OF TRAINING:

WEATHER: | TEMPERATURE:

TASK TYPE:

DURATION: | TREAT USED:

COMPETENCE: ☐ 1 ☐ 2 ☐ 3 ☐ 4 ☐ 5 ☐ 6 ☐ 7 ☐ 8 ☐ 9 ☐ 1(

SUCCESS:

NEEDS IMPROVEMENT:

NOTES:

TRAINING LOG

DATE: TIME: HANDLER:

LOCATION: TYPE OF TRAINING:

WEATHER: TEMPERATURE:

TASK TYPE:

DURATION: TREAT USED:

COMPETENCE: □ 1   □ 2   □ 3   □ 4   □ 5   □ 6   □ 7   □ 8   □ 9   □ 10

SUCCESS:

NEEDS IMPROVEMENT:

NOTES:

DATE: TIME: HANDLER:

LOCATION: TYPE OF TRAINING:

WEATHER: TEMPERATURE:

TASK TYPE:

DURATION: TREAT USED:

COMPETENCE: □ 1   □ 2   □ 3   □ 4   □ 5   □ 6   □ 7   □ 8   □ 9   □ 10

SUCCESS:

NEEDS IMPROVEMENT:

NOTES:

TRAINING LOG

DATE: TIME: HANDLER:

LOCATION: TYPE OF TRAINING:

WEATHER: TEMPERATURE:

TASK TYPE:

DURATION: TREAT USED:

COMPETENCE: ☐ 1   ☐ 2   ☐ 3   ☐ 4   ☐ 5   ☐ 6   ☐ 7   ☐ 8   ☐ 9   ☐ 10

SUCCESS:

NEEDS IMPROVEMENT:

NOTES:

DATE: TIME: HANDLER:

LOCATION: TYPE OF TRAINING:

WEATHER: TEMPERATURE:

TASK TYPE:

DURATION: TREAT USED:

COMPETENCE: ☐ 1   ☐ 2   ☐ 3   ☐ 4   ☐ 5   ☐ 6   ☐ 7   ☐ 8   ☐ 9   ☐ 10

SUCCESS:

NEEDS IMPROVEMENT:

NOTES:

TRAINING LOG

DATE: | TIME: | HANDLER:

LOCATION: | TYPE OF TRAINING:

WEATHER: | TEMPERATURE:

TASK TYPE:

DURATION: | TREAT USED:

COMPETENCE: □ 1　□ 2　□ 3　□ 4　□ 5　□ 6　□ 7　□ 8　□ 9　□ 10

SUCCESS:

NEEDS IMPROVEMENT:

NOTES:

DATE: | TIME: | HANDLER:

LOCATION: | TYPE OF TRAINING:

WEATHER: | TEMPERATURE:

TASK TYPE:

DURATION: | TREAT USED:

COMPETENCE: □ 1　□ 2　□ 3　□ 4　□ 5　□ 6　□ 7　□ 8　□ 9　□ 10

SUCCESS:

NEEDS IMPROVEMENT:

NOTES:

TRAINING LOG

DATE: | TIME: | HANDLER:

LOCATION: | TYPE OF TRAINING:

WEATHER: | TEMPERATURE:

TASK TYPE:

DURATION: | TREAT USED:

COMPETENCE: □ 1 □ 2 □ 3 □ 4 □ 5 □ 6 □ 7 □ 8 □ 9 □10

SUCCESS:

NEEDS IMPROVEMENT:

NOTES:

DATE: | TIME: | HANDLER:

LOCATION: | TYPE OF TRAINING:

WEATHER: | TEMPERATURE:

TASK TYPE:

DURATION: | TREAT USED:

COMPETENCE: □ 1 □ 2 □ 3 □ 4 □ 5 □ 6 □ 7 □ 8 □ 9 □ 1

SUCCESS:

NEEDS IMPROVEMENT:

NOTES:

TRAINING LOG

DATE: TIME: HANDLER:

LOCATION: TYPE OF TRAINING:

WEATHER: TEMPERATURE:

TASK TYPE:

DURATION: TREAT USED:

COMPETENCE: □ 1   □ 2   □ 3   □ 4   □ 5   □ 6   □ 7   □ 8   □ 9   □ 10

SUCCESS:

NEEDS IMPROVEMENT:

NOTES:

DATE: TIME: HANDLER:

LOCATION: TYPE OF TRAINING:

WEATHER: TEMPERATURE:

TASK TYPE:

DURATION: TREAT USED:

COMPETENCE: □ 1   □ 2   □ 3   □ 4   □ 5   □ 6   □ 7   □ 8   □ 9   □ 10

SUCCESS:

NEEDS IMPROVEMENT:

NOTES:

TRAINING LOG

DATE: | TIME: | HANDLER:

LOCATION: | TYPE OF TRAINING:

WEATHER: | TEMPERATURE:

TASK TYPE:

DURATION: | TREAT USED:

COMPETENCE: □ 1　□ 2　□ 3　□ 4　□ 5　□ 6　□ 7　□ 8　□ 9　□ 10

SUCCESS:

NEEDS IMPROVEMENT:

NOTES:

DATE: | TIME: | HANDLER:

LOCATION: | TYPE OF TRAINING:

WEATHER: | TEMPERATURE:

TASK TYPE:

DURATION: | TREAT USED:

COMPETENCE: □ 1　□ 2　□ 3　□ 4　□ 5　□ 6　□ 7　□ 8　□ 9　□ 1C

SUCCESS:

NEEDS IMPROVEMENT:

NOTES:

TRAINING LOG

DATE: TIME: HANDLER:

LOCATION: TYPE OF TRAINING:

WEATHER: TEMPERATURE:

TASK TYPE:

DURATION: TREAT USED:

COMPETENCE: □ 1   □ 2   □ 3   □ 4   □ 5   □ 6   □ 7   □ 8   □ 9   □ 10

SUCCESS:

NEEDS IMPROVEMENT:

NOTES:

DATE: TIME: HANDLER:

LOCATION: TYPE OF TRAINING:

WEATHER: TEMPERATURE:

TASK TYPE:

DURATION: TREAT USED:

COMPETENCE: □ 1   □ 2   □ 3   □ 4   □ 5   □ 6   □ 7   □ 8   □ 9   □ 10

SUCCESS:

NEEDS IMPROVEMENT:

NOTES:

TRAINING LOG

DATE: | TIME: | HANDLER:

LOCATION: | TYPE OF TRAINING:

WEATHER: | TEMPERATURE:

TASK TYPE:

DURATION: | TREAT USED:

COMPETENCE: □ 1 □ 2 □ 3 □ 4 □ 5 □ 6 □ 7 □ 8 □ 9 □ 10

SUCCESS:

NEEDS IMPROVEMENT:

NOTES:

DATE: | TIME: | HANDLER:

LOCATION: | TYPE OF TRAINING:

WEATHER: | TEMPERATURE:

TASK TYPE:

DURATION: | TREAT USED:

COMPETENCE: □ 1 □ 2 □ 3 □ 4 □ 5 □ 6 □ 7 □ 8 □ 9 □ 10

SUCCESS:

NEEDS IMPROVEMENT:

NOTES:

TRAINING LOG

DATE: TIME: HANDLER:

LOCATION: TYPE OF TRAINING:

WEATHER: TEMPERATURE:

TASK TYPE:

DURATION: TREAT USED:

COMPETENCE: □ 1   □ 2   □ 3   □ 4   □ 5   □ 6   □ 7   □ 8   □ 9   □ 10

SUCCESS:

NEEDS IMPROVEMENT:

NOTES:

DATE: TIME: HANDLER:

LOCATION: TYPE OF TRAINING:

WEATHER: TEMPERATURE:

TASK TYPE:

DURATION: TREAT USED:

COMPETENCE: □ 1   □ 2   □ 3   □ 4   □ 5   □ 6   □ 7   □ 8   □ 9   □ 10

SUCCESS:

NEEDS IMPROVEMENT:

NOTES:

TRAINING LOG

DATE: | TIME: | HANDLER:

LOCATION: | TYPE OF TRAINING:

WEATHER: | TEMPERATURE:

TASK TYPE:

DURATION: | TREAT USED:

COMPETENCE: □ 1 □ 2 □ 3 □ 4 □ 5 □ 6 □ 7 □ 8 □ 9 □10

SUCCESS:

NEEDS IMPROVEMENT:

NOTES:

DATE: | TIME: | HANDLER:

LOCATION: | TYPE OF TRAINING:

WEATHER: | TEMPERATURE:

TASK TYPE:

DURATION: | TREAT USED:

COMPETENCE: □ 1 □ 2 □ 3 □ 4 □ 5 □ 6 □ 7 □ 8 □ 9 □ 1

SUCCESS:

NEEDS IMPROVEMENT:

NOTES:

TRAINING LOG

DATE: TIME: HANDLER:

LOCATION: TYPE OF TRAINING:

WEATHER: TEMPERATURE:

TASK TYPE:

DURATION: TREAT USED:

COMPETENCE: □ 1   □ 2   □ 3   □ 4   □ 5   □ 6   □ 7   □ 8   □ 9   □ 10

SUCCESS:

NEEDS IMPROVEMENT:

NOTES:

DATE: TIME: HANDLER:

LOCATION: TYPE OF TRAINING:

WEATHER: TEMPERATURE:

TASK TYPE:

DURATION: TREAT USED:

COMPETENCE: □ 1   □ 2   □ 3   □ 4   □ 5   □ 6   □ 7   □ 8   □ 9   □ 10

SUCCESS:

NEEDS IMPROVEMENT:

NOTES:

TRAINING LOG

DATE: | TIME: | HANDLER:

LOCATION: | TYPE OF TRAINING:

WEATHER: | TEMPERATURE:

TASK TYPE:

DURATION: | TREAT USED:

COMPETENCE: □ 1 □ 2 □ 3 □ 4 □ 5 □ 6 □ 7 □ 8 □ 9 □ 10

SUCCESS:

NEEDS IMPROVEMENT:

NOTES:

DATE: | TIME: | HANDLER:

LOCATION: | TYPE OF TRAINING:

WEATHER: | TEMPERATURE:

TASK TYPE:

DURATION: | TREAT USED:

COMPETENCE: □ 1 □ 2 □ 3 □ 4 □ 5 □ 6 □ 7 □ 8 □ 9 □ 10

SUCCESS:

NEEDS IMPROVEMENT:

NOTES:

TRAINING LOG

DATE: | TIME: | HANDLER:

LOCATION: | TYPE OF TRAINING:

WEATHER: | TEMPERATURE:

TASK TYPE:

DURATION: | TREAT USED:

COMPETENCE: □ 1 □ 2 □ 3 □ 4 □ 5 □ 6 □ 7 □ 8 □ 9 □ 10

SUCCESS:

NEEDS IMPROVEMENT:

NOTES:

DATE: | TIME: | HANDLER:

LOCATION: | TYPE OF TRAINING:

WEATHER: | TEMPERATURE:

TASK TYPE:

DURATION: | TREAT USED:

COMPETENCE: □ 1 □ 2 □ 3 □ 4 □ 5 □ 6 □ 7 □ 8 □ 9 □ 10

SUCCESS:

NEEDS IMPROVEMENT:

NOTES:

TRAINING LOG

DATE: TIME: HANDLER:

LOCATION: TYPE OF TRAINING:

WEATHER: TEMPERATURE:

TASK TYPE:

DURATION: TREAT USED:

COMPETENCE: □ 1   □ 2   □ 3   □ 4   □ 5   □ 6   □ 7   □ 8   □ 9   □ 10

SUCCESS:

NEEDS IMPROVEMENT:

NOTES:

DATE: TIME: HANDLER:

LOCATION: TYPE OF TRAINING:

WEATHER: TEMPERATURE:

TASK TYPE:

DURATION: TREAT USED:

COMPETENCE: □ 1   □ 2   □ 3   □ 4   □ 5   □ 6   □ 7   □ 8   □ 9   □ 10

SUCCESS:

NEEDS IMPROVEMENT:

NOTES:

TRAINING LOG

DATE: _____ TIME: _____ HANDLER: _____

LOCATION: _____ TYPE OF TRAINING: _____

WEATHER: _____ TEMPERATURE: _____

TASK TYPE: _____

DURATION: _____ TREAT USED: _____

COMPETENCE: □ 1 □ 2 □ 3 □ 4 □ 5 □ 6 □ 7 □ 8 □ 9 □10

SUCCESS: _____

NEEDS IMPROVEMENT: _____

NOTES: _____

DATE: _____ TIME: _____ HANDLER: _____

LOCATION: _____ TYPE OF TRAINING: _____

WEATHER: _____ TEMPERATURE: _____

TASK TYPE: _____

DURATION: _____ TREAT USED: _____

COMPETENCE: □ 1 □ 2 □ 3 □ 4 □ 5 □ 6 □ 7 □ 8 □ 9 □10

SUCCESS: _____

NEEDS IMPROVEMENT: _____

NOTES: _____

TRAINING LOG

DATE: TIME: HANDLER:

LOCATION: TYPE OF TRAINING:

WEATHER: TEMPERATURE:

TASK TYPE:

DURATION: TREAT USED:

COMPETENCE: □ 1   □ 2   □ 3   □ 4   □ 5   □ 6   □ 7   □ 8   □ 9   □ 10

SUCCESS:

NEEDS IMPROVEMENT:

NOTES:

DATE: TIME: HANDLER:

LOCATION: TYPE OF TRAINING:

WEATHER: TEMPERATURE:

TASK TYPE:

DURATION: TREAT USED:

COMPETENCE: □ 1   □ 2   □ 3   □ 4   □ 5   □ 6   □ 7   □ 8   □ 9   □ 1

SUCCESS:

NEEDS IMPROVEMENT:

NOTES:

TRAINING LOG

DATE: TIME: HANDLER:

LOCATION: TYPE OF TRAINING:

WEATHER: TEMPERATURE:

TASK TYPE:

DURATION: TREAT USED:

COMPETENCE: □ 1   □ 2   □ 3   □ 4   □ 5   □ 6   □ 7   □ 8   □ 9   □ 10

SUCCESS:

NEEDS IMPROVEMENT:

NOTES:

DATE: TIME: HANDLER:

LOCATION: TYPE OF TRAINING:

WEATHER: TEMPERATURE:

TASK TYPE:

DURATION: TREAT USED:

COMPETENCE: □ 1   □ 2   □ 3   □ 4   □ 5   □ 6   □ 7   □ 8   □ 9   □ 10

SUCCESS:

NEEDS IMPROVEMENT:

NOTES:

TRAINING LOG

DATE: TIME: HANDLER:

LOCATION: TYPE OF TRAINING:

WEATHER: TEMPERATURE:

TASK TYPE:

DURATION: TREAT USED:

COMPETENCE: □ 1   □ 2   □ 3   □ 4   □ 5   □ 6   □ 7   □ 8   □ 9   □ 10

SUCCESS:

NEEDS IMPROVEMENT:

NOTES:

DATE: TIME: HANDLER:

LOCATION: TYPE OF TRAINING:

WEATHER: TEMPERATURE:

TASK TYPE:

DURATION: TREAT USED:

COMPETENCE: □ 1   □ 2   □ 3   □ 4   □ 5   □ 6   □ 7   □ 8   □ 9   □ 10

SUCCESS:

NEEDS IMPROVEMENT:

NOTES:

TRAINING LOG

DATE: TIME: HANDLER:

LOCATION: TYPE OF TRAINING:

WEATHER: TEMPERATURE:

TASK TYPE:

DURATION: TREAT USED:

COMPETENCE: □ 1   □ 2   □ 3   □ 4   □ 5   □ 6   □ 7   □ 8   □ 9   □ 10

SUCCESS:

NEEDS IMPROVEMENT:

NOTES:

DATE: TIME: HANDLER:

LOCATION: TYPE OF TRAINING:

WEATHER: TEMPERATURE:

TASK TYPE:

DURATION: TREAT USED:

COMPETENCE: □ 1   □ 2   □ 3   □ 4   □ 5   □ 6   □ 7   □ 8   □ 9   □ 10

SUCCESS:

NEEDS IMPROVEMENT:

NOTES:

TRAINING LOG

DATE: TIME: HANDLER:

LOCATION: TYPE OF TRAINING:

WEATHER: TEMPERATURE:

TASK TYPE:

DURATION: TREAT USED:

COMPETENCE: □ 1   □ 2   □ 3   □ 4   □ 5   □ 6   □ 7   □ 8   □ 9   □ 10

SUCCESS:

NEEDS IMPROVEMENT:

NOTES:

DATE: TIME: HANDLER:

LOCATION: TYPE OF TRAINING:

WEATHER: TEMPERATURE:

TASK TYPE:

DURATION: TREAT USED:

COMPETENCE: □ 1   □ 2   □ 3   □ 4   □ 5   □ 6   □ 7   □ 8   □ 9   □ 10

SUCCESS:

NEEDS IMPROVEMENT:

NOTES:

TRAINING LOG

DATE: | TIME: | HANDLER:

LOCATION: | TYPE OF TRAINING:

WEATHER: | TEMPERATURE:

TASK TYPE:

DURATION: | TREAT USED:

COMPETENCE: □ 1　□ 2　□ 3　□ 4　□ 5　□ 6　□ 7　□ 8　□ 9　□ 10

SUCCESS:

NEEDS IMPROVEMENT:

NOTES:

DATE: | TIME: | HANDLER:

LOCATION: | TYPE OF TRAINING:

WEATHER: | TEMPERATURE:

TASK TYPE:

DURATION: | TREAT USED:

COMPETENCE: □ 1　□ 2　□ 3　□ 4　□ 5　□ 6　□ 7　□ 8　□ 9　□ 10

SUCCESS:

NEEDS IMPROVEMENT:

NOTES:

TRAINING LOG

DATE: | TIME: | HANDLER:

LOCATION: | TYPE OF TRAINING:

WEATHER: | TEMPERATURE:

TASK TYPE:

DURATION: | TREAT USED:

COMPETENCE: □ 1 □ 2 □ 3 □ 4 □ 5 □ 6 □ 7 □ 8 □ 9 □ 10

SUCCESS:

NEEDS IMPROVEMENT:

NOTES:

DATE: | TIME: | HANDLER:

LOCATION: | TYPE OF TRAINING:

WEATHER: | TEMPERATURE:

TASK TYPE:

DURATION: | TREAT USED:

COMPETENCE: □ 1 □ 2 □ 3 □ 4 □ 5 □ 6 □ 7 □ 8 □ 9 □ 1

SUCCESS:

NEEDS IMPROVEMENT:

NOTES:

TRAINING LOG

DATE: TIME: HANDLER:

LOCATION: TYPE OF TRAINING:

WEATHER: TEMPERATURE:

TASK TYPE:

DURATION: TREAT USED:

COMPETENCE: □ 1   □ 2   □ 3   □ 4   □ 5   □ 6   □ 7   □ 8   □ 9   □ 10

SUCCESS:

NEEDS IMPROVEMENT:

NOTES:

DATE: TIME: HANDLER:

LOCATION: TYPE OF TRAINING:

WEATHER: TEMPERATURE:

TASK TYPE:

DURATION: TREAT USED:

COMPETENCE: □ 1   □ 2   □ 3   □ 4   □ 5   □ 6   □ 7   □ 8   □ 9   □ 10

SUCCESS:

NEEDS IMPROVEMENT:

NOTES:

TRAINING LOG

DATE: | TIME: | HANDLER:

LOCATION: | TYPE OF TRAINING:

WEATHER: | TEMPERATURE:

TASK TYPE:

DURATION: | TREAT USED:

COMPETENCE: □ 1 □ 2 □ 3 □ 4 □ 5 □ 6 □ 7 □ 8 □ 9 □ 10

SUCCESS:

NEEDS IMPROVEMENT:

NOTES:

DATE: | TIME: | HANDLER:

LOCATION: | TYPE OF TRAINING:

WEATHER: | TEMPERATURE:

TASK TYPE:

DURATION: | TREAT USED:

COMPETENCE: □ 1 □ 2 □ 3 □ 4 □ 5 □ 6 □ 7 □ 8 □ 9 □ 10

SUCCESS:

NEEDS IMPROVEMENT:

NOTES:

TRAINING LOG

DATE: | TIME: | HANDLER:

LOCATION: | TYPE OF TRAINING:

WEATHER: | TEMPERATURE:

TASK TYPE:

DURATION: | TREAT USED:

COMPETENCE: □ 1 □ 2 □ 3 □ 4 □ 5 □ 6 □ 7 □ 8 □ 9 □ 10

SUCCESS:

NEEDS IMPROVEMENT:

NOTES:

DATE: | TIME: | HANDLER:

LOCATION: | TYPE OF TRAINING:

WEATHER: | TEMPERATURE:

TASK TYPE:

DURATION: | TREAT USED:

COMPETENCE: □ 1 □ 2 □ 3 □ 4 □ 5 □ 6 □ 7 □ 8 □ 9 □ 10

SUCCESS:

NEEDS IMPROVEMENT:

NOTES:

CONTACT INFORMATION

VET INFO:

CLINIC:

VET NAME:

PHONE #:

AFTER HOURS PHONE #:

ADDRESS:

OWNER INFO:

NAME: Jessica Lewis

PHONE #: 512·963·1013

WORK #:

CPSIA information can be obtained
at www.ICGtesting.com
Printed in the USA
LVHW040458300920
667478LV00007B/961

9 781649 441614